POEMS TO SAVE THE WORLD WITH

Also by Chris Riddell
and available from Macmillan

Poems To Live Your Life By

Poems to Fall in Love With

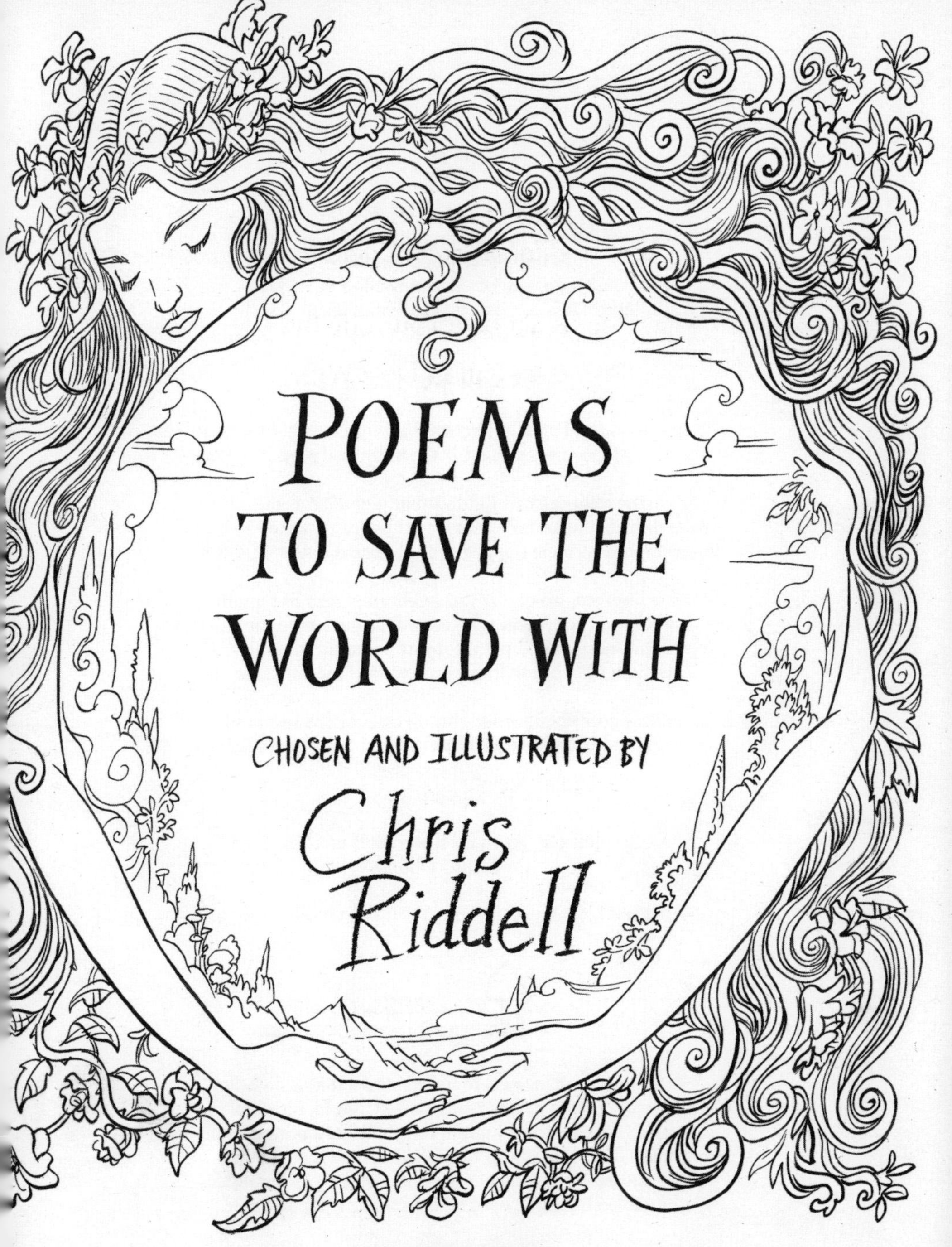
POEMS
TO SAVE THE
WORLD WITH
CHOSEN AND ILLUSTRATED BY
Chris
Riddell

MACMILLAN

First published 2020 by Macmillan Children's Books
an imprint of Pan Macmillan
The Smithson, 6 Briset Street, London EC1M 5NR
Associated companies throughout the world
www.panmacmillan.com

ISBN 978-1-5290-4011-1

1 3 5 7 9 8 6 4 2

A CIP catalogue record for this book is available from
the British Library.

Printed and bound by CPI Group (UK) Ltd, Croydon CR0 4YY

Contents

Lockdown

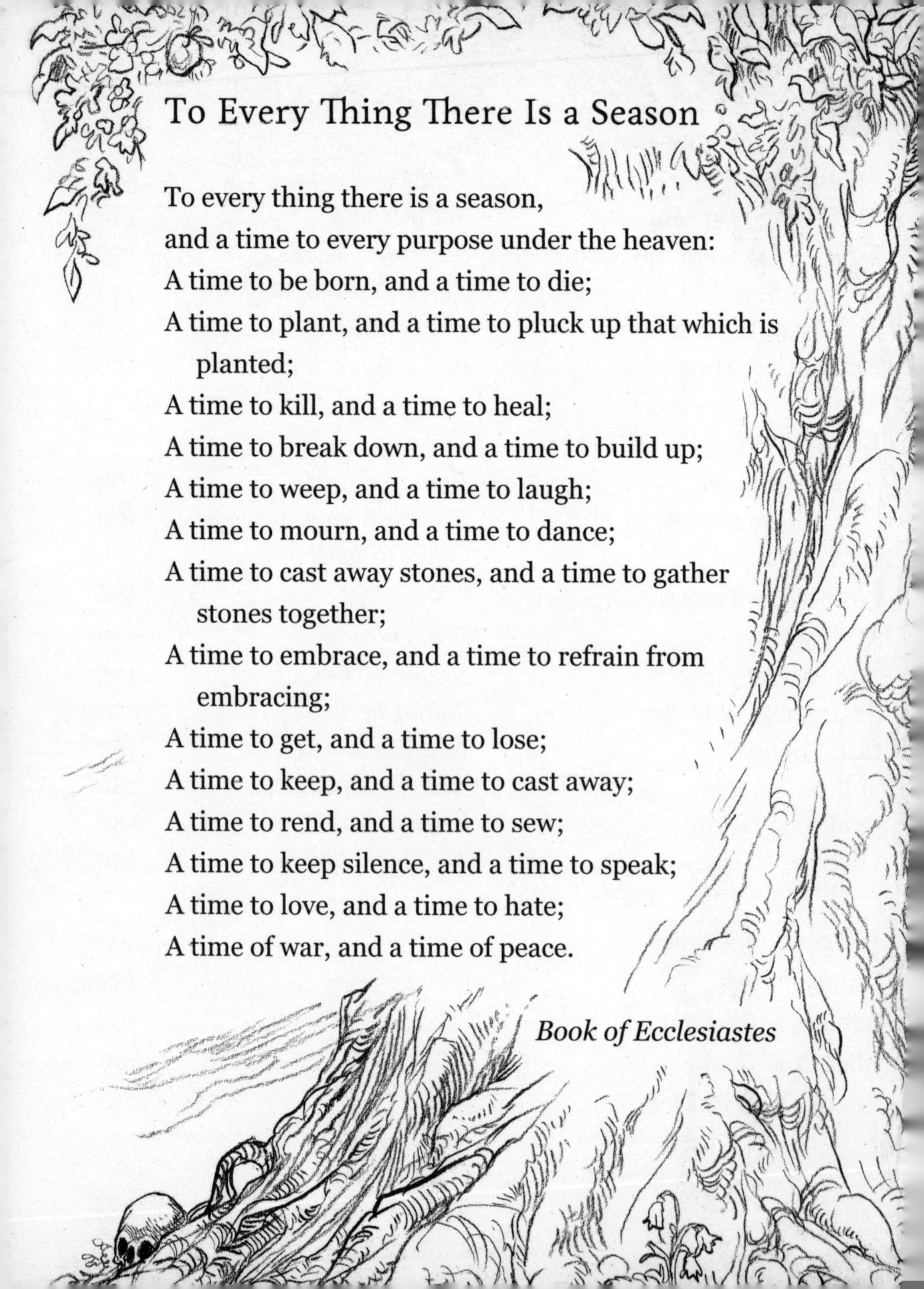

To Every Thing There Is a Season

To every thing there is a season,
and a time to every purpose under the heaven:
A time to be born, and a time to die;
A time to plant, and a time to pluck up that which is
planted;
A time to kill, and a time to heal;
A time to break down, and a time to build up;
A time to weep, and a time to laugh;
A time to mourn, and a time to dance;
A time to cast away stones, and a time to gather
stones together;
A time to embrace, and a time to refrain from
embracing;
A time to get, and a time to lose;
A time to keep, and a time to cast away;
A time to rend, and a time to sew;
A time to keep silence, and a time to speak;
A time to love, and a time to hate;
A time of war, and a time of peace.

Book of Ecclesiastes

HAPPY
THOUGHTS

Happy Thought

The world is so full
    of a number of things,
I'm sure we should all
    be as happy as kings.

Robert Louis Stevenson

Happy the Man

Happy the man, and happy he alone,
He who can call today his own:
He who, secure within, can say,
Tomorrow, do thy worst, for I have lived today.

John Dryden

WITH
ONLY
ONE LIFE

With Only One Life

Hold with both hands
The tray of every day
And pass in turn
Along this counter.

There is enough sun
For everybody.
There is enough sky,
And there is moon enough.

The earth gives off the smell
Of luck, of happiness, of glory,
Which tickles your nostrils
Temptingly.

So don't be miserly,
Live after your own heart.
The prices are derisory.

For instance, with only one life
You can acquire
The most beautiful woman,
Plus a biscuit.

Marin Sorescu
Translated from the Romanian by
D. J. Enright with Iona Russell-Gebbett

My Lover Eats Words For Supper

and there's music for dinner
soft melody melting away at touch
sprinkle some hellos for seasoning
a scoop of 'how was your day?'
the clink clink of plates
a clatter of spoons, forks, silence
words condense into nothingness
fade away at dawn
are boiled in hot water
gobbled up with rice
we do not speak here
we have nothing to say
love is only a metaphor
syllables lurk inside cupboards
silverware rattles
fills the house with noise
a distant orchestra hums

Khushi Daryani

from Auguries of Innocence

To see a World in a Grain of Sand
And a Heaven in a Wild Flower,
Hold Infinity in the palm of your hand
And Eternity in an hour.

William Blake

‘Hope’ is the Thing with Feathers

‘Hope’ is the thing with feathers –
That perches in the soul –
And sings the tune without the words –
And never stops – at all –

And sweetest – in the Gale – is heard –
And sore must be the storm –
That could abash the little Bird
That kept so many warm –

I’ve heard it in the chillest land –
And on the strangest Sea –
Yet, never, in Extremity,
It asked a crumb – of Me.

Emily Dickinson

Wild Geese

You do not have to be good.
You do not have to walk on your knees
for a hundred miles through the desert, repenting.
You only have to let the soft animal of your body
love what it loves.
Tell me about despair, yours, and I will tell you mine.
Meanwhile the world goes on.
Meanwhile the sun and the clear pebbles of the rain
are moving across the landscapes,
over the prairies and the deep trees,
the mountains and the rivers.
Meanwhile the wild geese, high in the clean blue air,
are heading home again.
Whoever you are, no matter how lonely,
the world offers itself to your imagination,
calls to you like the wild geese, harsh and exciting –
over and over announcing your place
in the family of things.

Mary Oliver

Travelling

This is the spot:—how mildly does the sun
Shine in between the fading leaves! the air
In the habitual silence of this wood
Is more than silent: and this bed of heath,
Where shall we find so sweet a resting-place?
Come!—let me see thee sink into a dream
Of quiet thoughts,—protracted till thine eye
Be calm as water when the winds are gone
And no one can tell whither.—my sweet friend!
We two have had such happy hours together
That my heart melts in me to think of it.

William Wordsworth

Almond Blossom

This morning, love, I'm tired and grave;
I can barely hear the wintered bird's small song
over the hum of the central heating.
We must trust, I suppose, to the song's bare minim:

that spring will be a green havoc
as the trees burst their slums
and the dirt breaks open to admit
crocus-spear and cyclamen;

and though we can't yet feel it
earth's already begun
her slow incline, inch by ruined inch,
easing you back from the brink.

Fiona Benson

The Hubble Space Telescope before repair

The way they tell it
All the stars have wings
The sky so full of wings
There is no sky
And just for a moment
You forget
The error and the crimped
Paths of light
And you see it
The immense migration
And you hear the rush
The beating

Rebecca Elson

A Word of Advice

Stop falling in love with people you could write poems about.
Stop tripping over and drowning yourself in metaphors
And obsessing over similes
Like your silly white shirt is clouding your judgement.
Resist those with whom you can be Radcliffian,
Fall in love with no one in any way Byronic,
Or those who may resemble, in any sense, the rose.

Do not fall in love with someone who could
Drive you down a highway at night and
Make it feel like you were flying, dizzy
On the vitality and the necessity and the kissing
And the kissing and the kissing.
Minimize the ways in which your love is Italian,
And ensure that it is in no way French.
Just be a bit British about the whole thing.

Avoid great passion – keep your head.
It cannot end in anything
Better than a rhyming couplet.
Fall in love with someone who is prose at best.
Somebody you could write an article about –
A conversational, informational blog,
Someone fit for the BBC homepage on a Sunday:
Sticking to the facts with just a touch of emotion.

Perhaps find someone with clammy palms
So you won't mind letting go.
Someone who has kissing down to a fine art,
By which I mean, a neatly framed watercolour:
Firm pecks – you could call them sobering –
Lipless; polite, with just a touch of affection.
Don't get used to kissing in Kandinsky colours –
Find someone you can go grey with.

Hurdle the white picket fence and tumble
Through the window of a semi-detached,
Onto the sofa next to the sensible choice –
Someone you could take home to your mother –
Someone you can sit with, woodenly,
With the cat, and a cup of tea,
And *Songs of Praise* providing the soundtrack
To your domestic tedium.

Calm down. Grow up. Come to terms
With the fact that love like that
Just isn't for the likes of you.
It belongs to Other People, sealed away
Between the pages of an anthology
(Think *The Nation's Favourite Love Poems*),
Stowed secretly, adulterously, away in a nightstand.
Life will be sufficient, and you'll get along just fine,
Because a tree grown in the dark can never miss the sun.

Consider settling for someone you could safely live without,
But please – stop falling in love with people you could write
poems about.

Libby Russell

The Mushroom Hunters

Science, as you know, my little one, is the study
of the nature and behaviour of the universe.
It's based on observation, on experiment, and measurement,
and the formulation of laws to describe the facts revealed.

In the old times, they say, the men came already fitted with brains
designed to follow flesh-beasts at a run,
to hurdle blindly into the unknown,
and then to find their way back home when lost
with a slain antelope to carry between them.
Or, on bad hunting days, nothing.

The women, who did not need to run down prey,
had brains that spotted landmarks and made paths between them
left at the thorn bush and across the scree
and look down in the bole of the half-fallen tree,
because sometimes there are mushrooms.

Before the flint club, or flint butcher's tools,
The first tool of all was a sling for the baby
to keep our hands free
and something to put the berries and the mushrooms in,
the roots and the good leaves, the seeds and the crawlers.
Then a flint pestle to smash, to crush, to grind or break.

And sometimes men chased the beasts
into the deep woods,
and never came back.

Some mushrooms will kill you,
while some will show you gods
and some will feed the hunger in our bellies. Identify.

Others will kill us if we eat them raw,
and kill us again if we cook them once,
but if we boil them up in spring water, and pour the water away,
and then boil them once more, and pour the water away,
only then can we eat them safely. Observe.

Observe childbirth, measure the swell of bellies and the shape of breasts,
and through experience discover how to bring babies safely into the world.

Observe everything.

And the mushroom hunters walk the ways they walk
and watch the world, and see what they observe.
And some of them would thrive and lick their lips,
While others clutched their stomachs and expired.
So laws are made and handed down on what is safe. Formulate.

The tools we make to build our lives:
our clothes, our food, our path home . . .
all these things we base on observation,
on experiment, on measurement, on truth.

And science, you remember, is the study
of the nature and behaviour of the universe,
based on observation, experiment, and measurement,
and the formulation of laws to describe these facts.

The race continues. An early scientist
drew beasts upon the walls of caves
to show her children, now all fat on mushrooms
and on berries, what would be safe to hunt.

The men go running on after beasts.

The scientists walk more slowly, over to the brow of the hill
and down to the water's edge and past the place where the red
clay runs.
They are carrying their babies in the slings they made,
freeing their hands to pick the mushrooms.

Neil Gaiman

EVERYTHING
IS GOING
TO BE OK

Crow Baby

Everything plant-delicate. I'm scared to force your arms through your sleeves, It's like trying to put a little T-shirt on a crow. That's what it feels like. It feels like I've captured a crow and for some reason I'm trying to show that crow unconditional love. Only it keeps pecking me, flapping its wings and flying around the room and into walls, completely terrified, and I'm like, come on, crow, don't worry, I'm your father and I love you. Come and perch on my shoulder. And the crow just flies around the ceiling like a fan stuck on doublespeed – CAAAAAWWWWW! – stopping only when it reaches total exhaustion. And then I'm like, I love you. I love you, crow. I put the crow to my neck and I sit on a metallic grey exercise ball, the volume right down and subtitles on because love is so boring. I hum everything my dad used to play on the piano – stuff I didn't know I remembered. Crow, I whisper, bouncing ludicrously on the ball, I whisper what I will whisper five years later, crouched by a drunk man weeping on Hungerford Bridge, it's going to get better, it's going to get better and everything is going to be okay.

Luke Kennard

The Peace of Wild Things

When despair for the world grows in me
and I wake in the night at the least sound
in fear of what my life and children's lives may be,
I go and lie down where the wood drake
rests in his beauty on the water, and the great heron feeds.
I come into the peace of wild things
who do not tax their lives with forethought
of grief. I come into the presence of still water.
And I feel above me the day-blind stars
waiting with their light. For a time
I rest in the grace of the world, and am free.

Wendell Berry

Invictus

Out of the night that covers me,
 Black as the pit from pole to pole,
I thank whatever gods may be
 For my unconquerable soul.

In the fell clutch of circumstance
 I have not winced nor cried aloud.
Under the bludgeonings of chance
 My head is bloody, but unbowed.

Beyond this place of wrath and tears
 Looms but the Horror of the shade,
And yet the menace of the years
 Finds and shall find me unafraid.

It matters not how strait the gate,
 How charged with punishments the scroll,
I am the master of my fate,
 I am the captain of my soul.

W. E. Henley

Battle Call

I want to find the voice to speak the words.
I want to shape the air and let them sing.
I want to know the weightlessness of birds.
I want to feel that lift beneath the wing.

I want to keep those promises I made.
I want to meet the girl that I once knew.
I want to prove to her I'm not afraid.
I want to scale the summit for the view.

I want to learn the secrets of the sun.
I want to brave the hailstones as they fall.
I want to do all this. And when I'm done
I want the world to hear my battle call.

Rachel Rooney

Kindness

And maybe it is easier to learn kindness in these times.
When the whole world is like a small child with a fever,
trying her very best to make herself feel better.

Maybe we find our unity in the near-losing of everything.
Where we have no choice but to depend upon each other.
This is what it takes to realize we are in this together.

A man helps someone he dislikes because they are in danger.
A neighbour delivers groceries to everyone ill on her street.
Old friends forgive each other and stop acting like they are strangers.

Maybe this time, this is what the revolution looks like.
People helping each other despite their differences.
Understanding truly, that without the aid of others,

we would be all alone in this.

Nikita Gill

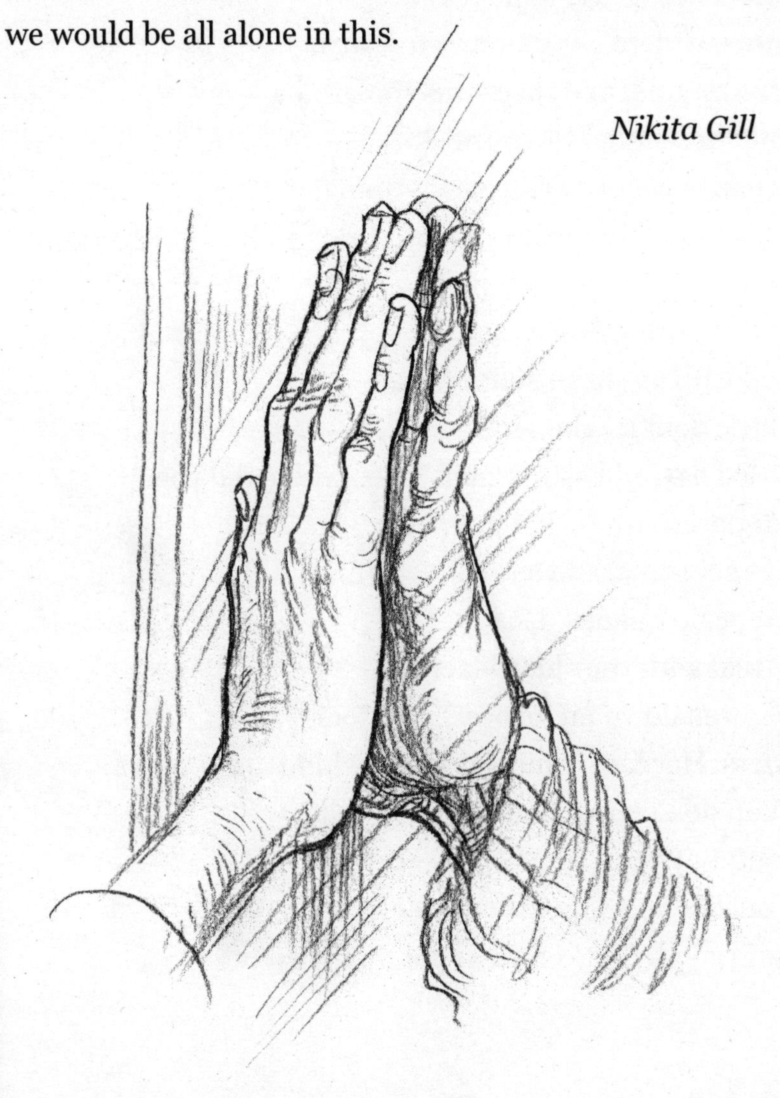

Departure Gate Aria

She was standing near a departure gate,
sandal-footed, her wiggly hair
and the latticework of her mercury footwear
the same satiny gold, and there was something
wistful about her, under the burnish
of her makeup she looked extremely young,
and a little afraid. I wanted to speak
to her, as if I were a guardian spirit
working the airport – God knows
I was crazed with my fresh solitariness –
so I did a little double take,
when I passed her, and said, Could I ask, where did you
get your sandals – my husband, I lied,
wants me to get some, and she said a name, as if
relieved to speak. Thanks, I said,
they look great with your hair – actually
(my head bowed down on its own), you look
like a goddess. Her face came out from behind
its cloud, You don't know how I needed that!,
she cried out, I'm going to meet my boyfriend's
parents. You'll do just fine, I said, you look
beautiful and good. She looked joyful. I bustled off –

so this is what I'll do, now,
instead of kissing and being kissed, I'll
go through airports praising people, like an
Antichrist saying, You do not need
to change your life.

Sharon Olds

What You Need to Be Warm

A baked potato of a winter's night to wrap your hands around
  or burn your mouth.
A blanket knitted by your mother's cunning fingers. Or your
  grandmother's.
A smile, a touch, trust, as you walk in from the snow
or return to it, the tips of your ears pricked pink and frozen.

The *tink tink tink* of iron radiators waking in an old house.
To surface from dreams in a bed, burrowed beneath blankets
and comforters,
the change of state from cold to warm is all that matters, and
you think
just one more minute snuggled here before you face the chill.
Just one.

Places we slept as children: they warm us in the memory.
We travel to an inside from the outside. To the orange flames of the fireplace
or the wood burning in the stove. Breath-ice on the inside of windows,
to be scratched off with a fingernail, melted with a whole hand.

Frost on the ground that stays in the shadows, waiting for us.
Wear a scarf. Wear a coat. Wear a sweater. Wear socks.
 Wear thick gloves.
An infant as she sleeps between us. A tumble of dogs,
a kindle of cats and kittens. Come inside. You're safe now.

A kettle boiling at the stove. Your family or friends are there.
They smile.
Cocoa or chocolate, tea or coffee, soup or toddy, what you know
you need.
A heat exchange, they give it to you, you take the mug
and start to thaw. While outside, for some of us, the journey
began

as we walked away from our grandparents' houses
away from the places we knew as children: changes of state and
state and state,
to stumble across a stony desert, or to brave the deep waters,
while food and friends, home, a bed, even a blanket become just
memories.

Sometimes it only takes a stranger, in a dark place,
to hold out a badly knitted scarf, to offer a kind word, to say
we have the right to be here, to make us warm in the coldest
season.

You have the right to be here.

Neil Gaiman

Neil Gaiman is a Goodwill Ambassador for UNHCR, the UN Refugee Agency. He originally wrote this poem in support of their Winter Emergency Appeal.

Otherwise

I got out of bed
on two strong legs.
It might have been
otherwise. I ate
cereal, sweet
milk, ripe, flawless
peach. It might
have been otherwise.
I took the dog uphill
to the birch wood.
All morning I did
the work I love.
At noon I lay down
with my mate. It might
have been otherwise.
We ate dinner together
at a table with silver
candlesticks. It might
have been otherwise.
I slept in a bed
in a room with paintings
on the walls, and
planned another day

just like this day.
But one day, I know,
It will be otherwise.

Jane Kenyon

Leisure

What is this life if, full of care,
We have no time to stand and stare?

No time to stand beneath the boughs
And stare as long as sheep or cows.

No time to see, when woods we pass,
Where squirrels hide their nuts in grass.

No time to see, in broad daylight,
Streams full of stars, like skies at night.

No time to turn at Beauty's glance,
And watch her feet, how they can dance.

No time to wait till her mouth can
Enrich that smile her eyes began.

A poor life this is if, full of care,
We have no time to stand and stare.

W. H. Davies

The Raincoat

When the doctor suggested surgery
and a brace for all my youngest years,
my parents scrambled to take me
to massage therapy, deep tissue work,
osteopathy, and soon my crooked spine
unspooled a bit, I could breathe again,
and move more in a body unclouded
by pain. My mom would tell me to sing
songs to her the whole forty-five-minute
drive to Middle Two Rock Road and forty-
five minutes back from physical therapy.
She'd say that even my voice sounded unfettered
by my spine afterward. So I sang and sang,
because I thought she liked it. I never
asked her what she gave up to drive me,
or how her day was before this chore. Today,
at her age, I was driving myself home from yet
another spine appointment, singing along
to some maudlin but solid song on the radio,
and I saw a mom take her raincoat off
and give it to her young daughter when
a storm took over the afternoon. My god,
I thought, my whole life I've been under her

raincoat thinking it was somehow a marvel
that I never got wet.

Ada Limón

Happy Birthday Moon

Dad reads aloud. I follow his finger across the page.
Sometimes his finger moves past words, tracing white space.
He makes the Moon say something new every night
to his deaf son who slurs his speech.

Sometimes his finger moves past words, tracing white space.
Tonight he gives the Moon my name, but I can't say it,
his deaf son who slurs his speech.
Dad taps the page, says, *try again*.

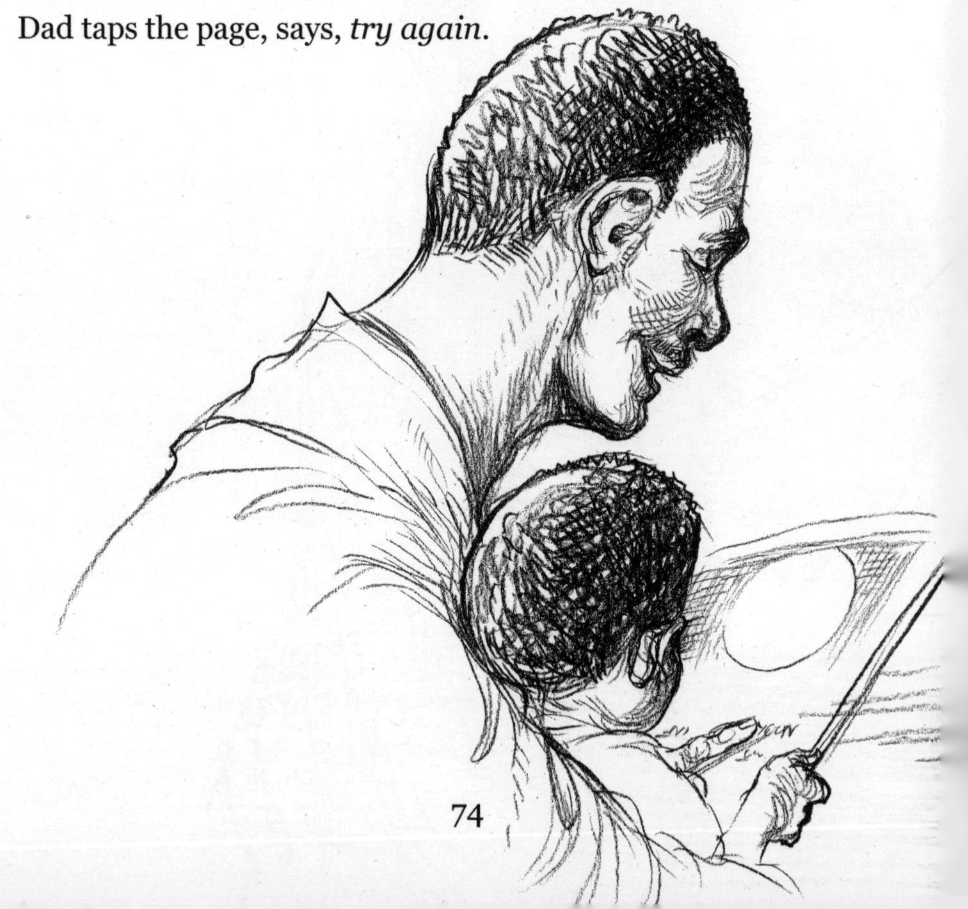

Tonight he gives the Moon my name, but I can't say it.
I say *Rain-nan Akabok.* He laughs.
Dad taps the page, says, *try again*,
but I like making him laugh. I say my mistake again.

I say *Rain-nan Akabok.* He laughs,
says, *Raymond you're something else.*
I like making him laugh. I say my mistake again.
Rain-nan Akabok. What else will help us?

He says, *Raymond you're something else.*
I'd like to be the Moon, the bear, even the rain.
Rain-nan Akabok, what else will help us
hear each other, really hear each other?

I'd like to be the Moon, the bear, even the rain.
Dad makes the Moon say something new every night
and we hear each other, really hear each other.
As Dad reads aloud, I follow his finger across the page.

Raymond Antrobus

If

If you can keep your head when all about you
  Are losing theirs and blaming it on you;
If you can trust yourself when all men doubt you,
  But make allowance for their doubting too;
If you can wait and not be tired by waiting,
  Or being lied about, don't deal in lies,
Or being hated, don't give way to hating,
  And yet don't look too good, nor talk too wise:

If you can dream – and not make dreams your master;
  If you can think – and not make thoughts your aim;
If you can meet with Triumph and Disaster
  And treat those two impostors just the same;
If you can bear to hear the truth you've spoken
  Twisted by knaves to make a trap for fools,
Or watch the things you gave your life to, broken,
  And stoop and build 'em up with worn-out tools:

If you can make one heap of all your winnings
  And risk it on one turn of pitch-and-toss,
And lose, and start again at your beginnings
  And never breathe a word about your loss;
If you can force your heart and nerve and sinew
  To serve your turn long after they are gone,
And so hold on when there is nothing in you
  Except the Will which says to them: 'Hold on!'

If you can talk with crowds and keep your virtue,
Or walk with Kings – nor lose the common touch,
If neither foes nor loving friends can hurt you,
If all men count with you, but none too much;
If you can fill the unforgiving minute
With sixty seconds' worth of distance run,
Yours is the Earth and everything that's in it,
And – which is more – you'll be a Man, my son!

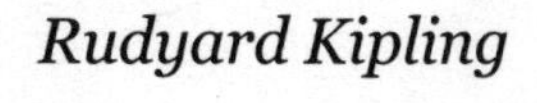

Rudyard Kipling

OH! I HAVE
SLIPPED THE SURLY
BONDS OF EARTH

High Flight

Oh! I have slipped the surly bonds of Earth
And danced the skies on laughter-silvered wings;
Sunward I've climbed, and joined the tumbling mirth
Of sun-split clouds, and done a hundred things
You have not dreamed of: wheeled and soared and swung
High in the sunlit silence. Hov'ring there,
I've chased the shouting wind along, and flung
My eager craft through footless halls of air . . .
Up, up the long, delirious burning blue
I've topped the wind-swept heights with easy grace
Where never lark, or even eagle flew –
And, while with silent, lifting mind I've trod
The high untrespassed sanctity of space,
Put out my hand, and touched the face of God.

John Gillespie Magee, Jr

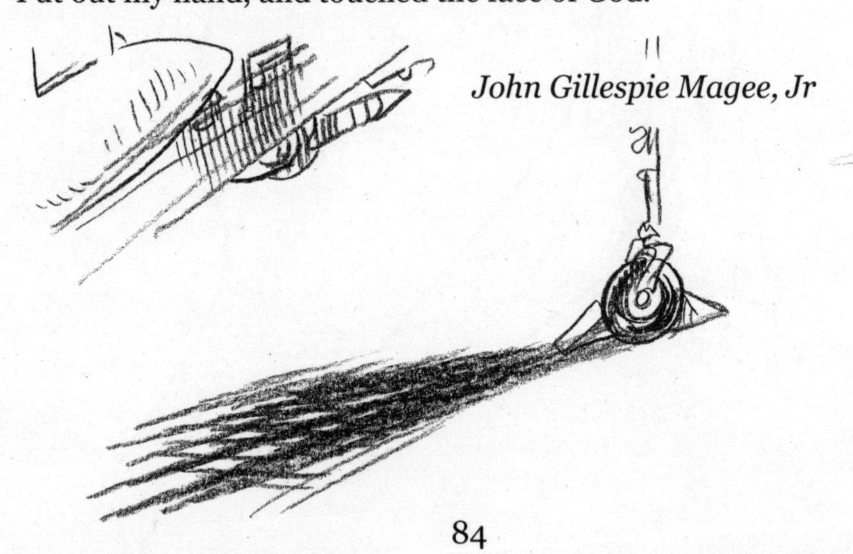

The Lake Isle of Innisfree

I will arise and go now, and go to Innisfree,
And a small cabin build there, of clay and wattles made:
Nine bean-rows will I have there, a hive for the honey-bee,
And live alone in the bee-loud glade.

And I shall have some peace there, for peace comes dropping slow,
Dropping from the veils of the morning to where the cricket sings;
There midnight's all a glimmer, and noon a purple glow,
And evening full of the linnet's wings.

I will arise and go now, for always night and day
I hear lake water lapping with low sounds by the shore;
While I stand on the roadway, or on the pavements grey,
I hear it in the deep heart's core.

W. B. Yeats

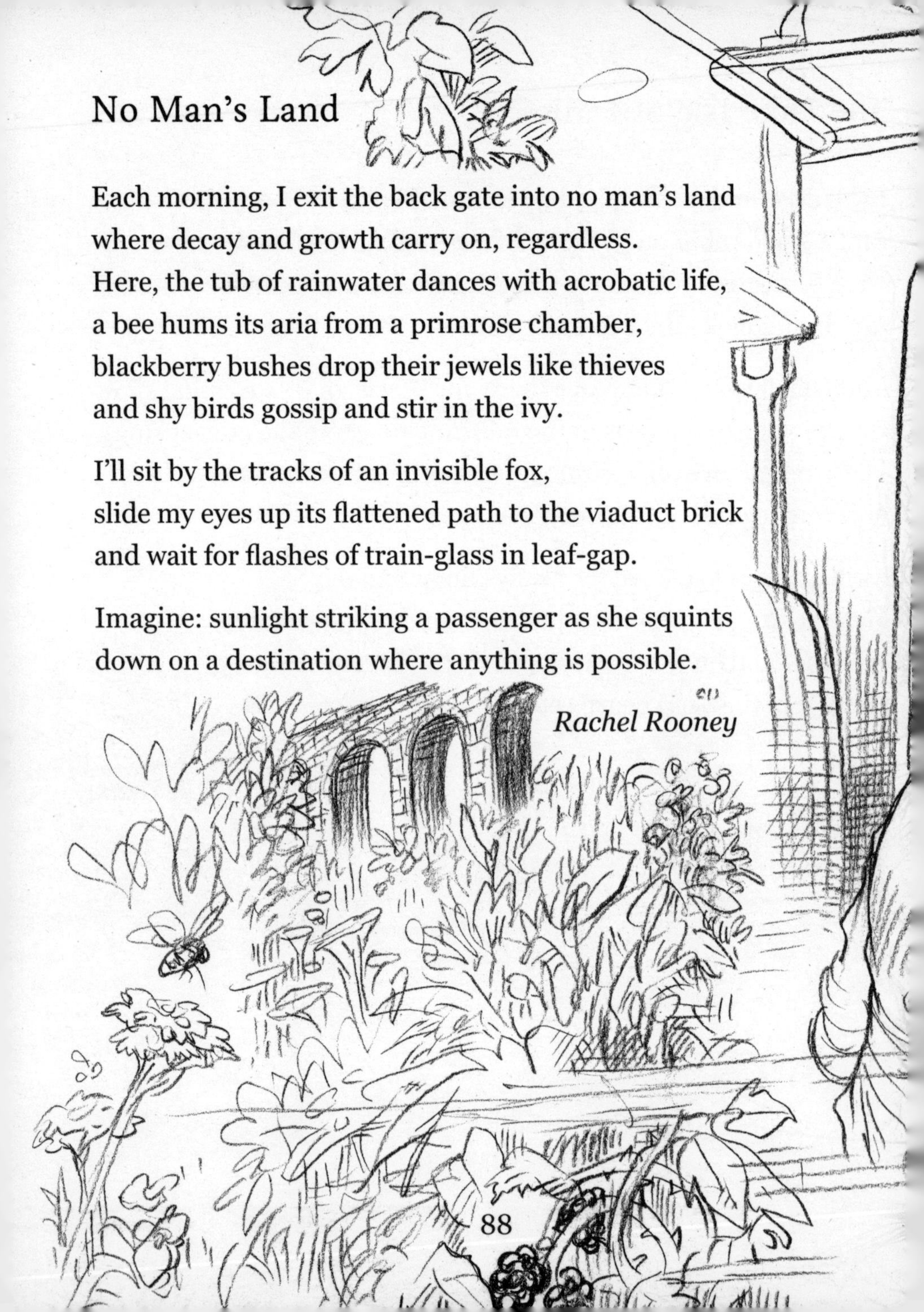

No Man's Land

Each morning, I exit the back gate into no man's land
where decay and growth carry on, regardless.
Here, the tub of rainwater dances with acrobatic life,
a bee hums its aria from a primrose chamber,
blackberry bushes drop their jewels like thieves
and shy birds gossip and stir in the ivy.

I'll sit by the tracks of an invisible fox,
slide my eyes up its flattened path to the viaduct brick
and wait for flashes of train-glass in leaf-gap.

Imagine: sunlight striking a passenger as she squints
down on a destination where anything is possible.

Rachel Rooney

SOUTHERN

Explaining Memes to Keats

So you see, I say slowly,
It's a little engine of remembering,
recalling, reverberating in the mind, like rhyme.
So, it can never die? he replies.
I avert my eyes.
It will, with time.

Nadia Lines

The Great Lover

I have been so great a lover: filled my days
So proudly with the splendour of Love's praise,
The pain, the calm, and the astonishment,
Desire illimitable, and still content,
And all dear names men use, to cheat despair,
For the perplexed and viewless streams that bear
Our hearts at random down the dark of life.
Now, ere the unthinking silence on that strife
Steals down, I would cheat drowsy Death so far,
My night shall be remembered for a star
That outshone all the suns of all men's days.
Shall I not crown them with immortal praise
Whom I have loved, who have given me, dared with me
High secrets, and in darkness knelt to see
The inenarrable godhead of delight?
Love is a flame:—we have beaconed the world's night.
A city:—and we have built it, these and I.
An emperor:—we have taught the world to die.
So, for their sakes I loved, ere I go hence,
And the high cause of Love's magnificence,
And to keep loyalties young, I'll write those names
Golden for ever, eagles, crying flames,
And set them as a banner, that men may know,

To dare the generations, burn, and blow
Out on the wind of Time, shining and streaming . . .

These I have loved:
White plates and cups, clean-gleaming,
Ringed with blue lines; and feathery, faery dust;
Wet roofs, beneath the lamp-light; the strong crust
Of friendly bread; and many-tasting food;
Rainbows; and the blue bitter smoke of wood;
And radiant raindrops couching in cool flowers;
And flowers themselves, that sway through sunny hours,
Dreaming of moths that drink them under the moon;
Then, the cool kindliness of sheets, that soon
Smooth away trouble; and the rough male kiss
Of blankets; grainy wood; live hair that is
Shining and free; blue-massing clouds; the keen
Unpassioned beauty of a great machine;
The benison of hot water; furs to touch;
The good smell of old clothes; and other such,
The comfortable smell of friendly fingers,
Hair's fragrance, and the musty reek that lingers
About dead leaves and last year's ferns . . .

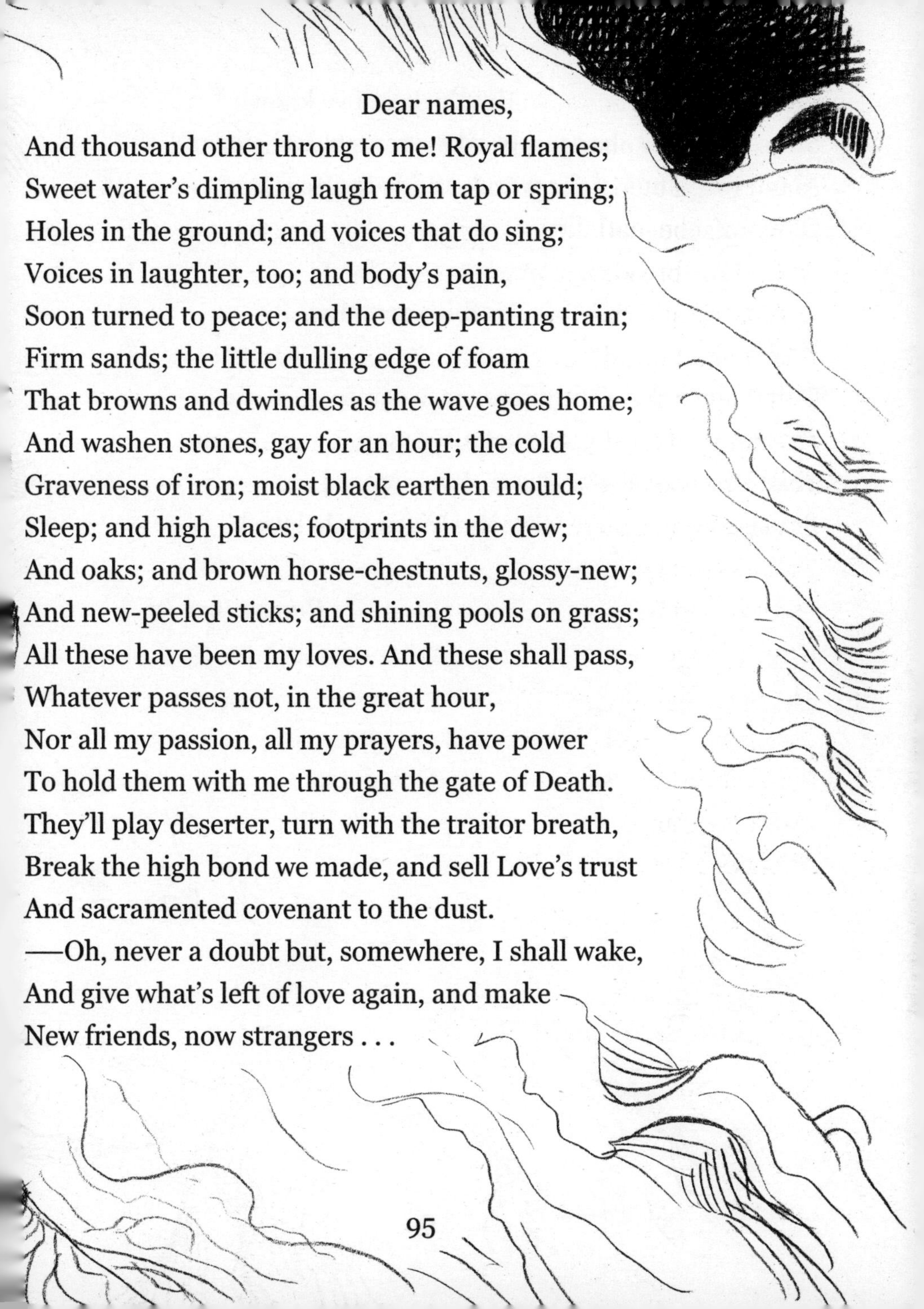

Dear names,
And thousand other throng to me! Royal flames;
Sweet water's dimpling laugh from tap or spring;
Holes in the ground; and voices that do sing;
Voices in laughter, too; and body's pain,
Soon turned to peace; and the deep-panting train;
Firm sands; the little dulling edge of foam
That browns and dwindles as the wave goes home;
And washen stones, gay for an hour; the cold
Graveness of iron; moist black earthen mould;
Sleep; and high places; footprints in the dew;
And oaks; and brown horse-chestnuts, glossy-new;
And new-peeled sticks; and shining pools on grass;
All these have been my loves. And these shall pass,
Whatever passes not, in the great hour,
Nor all my passion, all my prayers, have power
To hold them with me through the gate of Death.
They'll play deserter, turn with the traitor breath,
Break the high bond we made, and sell Love's trust
And sacramented covenant to the dust.
—Oh, never a doubt but, somewhere, I shall wake,
And give what's left of love again, and make
New friends, now strangers . . .

But the best I've known
Stays here, and changes, breaks, grows old, is blown
About the winds of the world, and fades from brains
Of living men, and dies.

Nothing remains.

O dear my loves, O faithless, once again
This one last gift I give: that after men
Shall know, and later lovers, far-removed,
Praise you, 'All these were lovely'; say, 'He loved.'

Rupert Brooke

There is no Frigate like a Book

There is no Frigate like a Book
To take us Lands away
Not any Coursers like a Page
Of prancing Poetry –
This Traverse may the poorest take
Without oppress of Toll –
How frugal is the Chariot
That bears the Human soul –

Emily Dickinson

from A Midsummer Night's Dream

I know a bank where the wild thyme blows,
Where oxlips and the nodding violet grows,
Quite over-canopied with luscious woodbine,
With sweet musk-roses and with eglantine:
There sleeps Titania sometime of the night,
Lulled in these flowers with dances and delight.

William Shakespeare

The Land of Counterpane

When I was sick and lay a-bed,
I had two pillows at my head,
And all my toys beside me lay
To keep me happy all the day.

And sometimes for an hour or so
I watched my leaden soldiers go,
With different uniforms and drills,
Among the bed-clothes, through the hills;

And sometimes sent my ships in fleets
All up and down among the sheets;
Or brought my trees and houses out,
And planted cities all about.

I was the giant great and still
That sits upon the pillow-hill,
And sees before him, dale and plain,
The pleasant land of counterpane.

Robert Louis Stevenson

The Tyger

Tyger Tyger, burning bright,
In the forests of the night;
What immortal hand or eye,
Could frame thy fearful symmetry?

In what distant deeps or skies
Burnt the fire of thine eyes!
On what wings dare he aspire?
What the hand, dare seize the fire?

And what shoulder, & what art,
Could twist the sinews of thy heart?
And when thy heart began to beat,
What dread hand? & what dread feet?

What the hammer? what the chain,
In what furnace was thy brain?
What the anvil? what dread grasp,
Dare its deadly terrors clasp?

When the stars threw down their spears
And water'd heaven with their tears:
Did he smile his work to see?
Did he who made the Lamb make thee?

Tyger, Tyger burning bright,
In the forests of the night:
What immortal hand or eye,
Dare frame thy fearful symmetry?

William Blake

Troll Song

‘It wasn’t always my ambition to live under a bridge.
There came a point though where a decision had to be made.
It was either here or in a swamp or a cave.

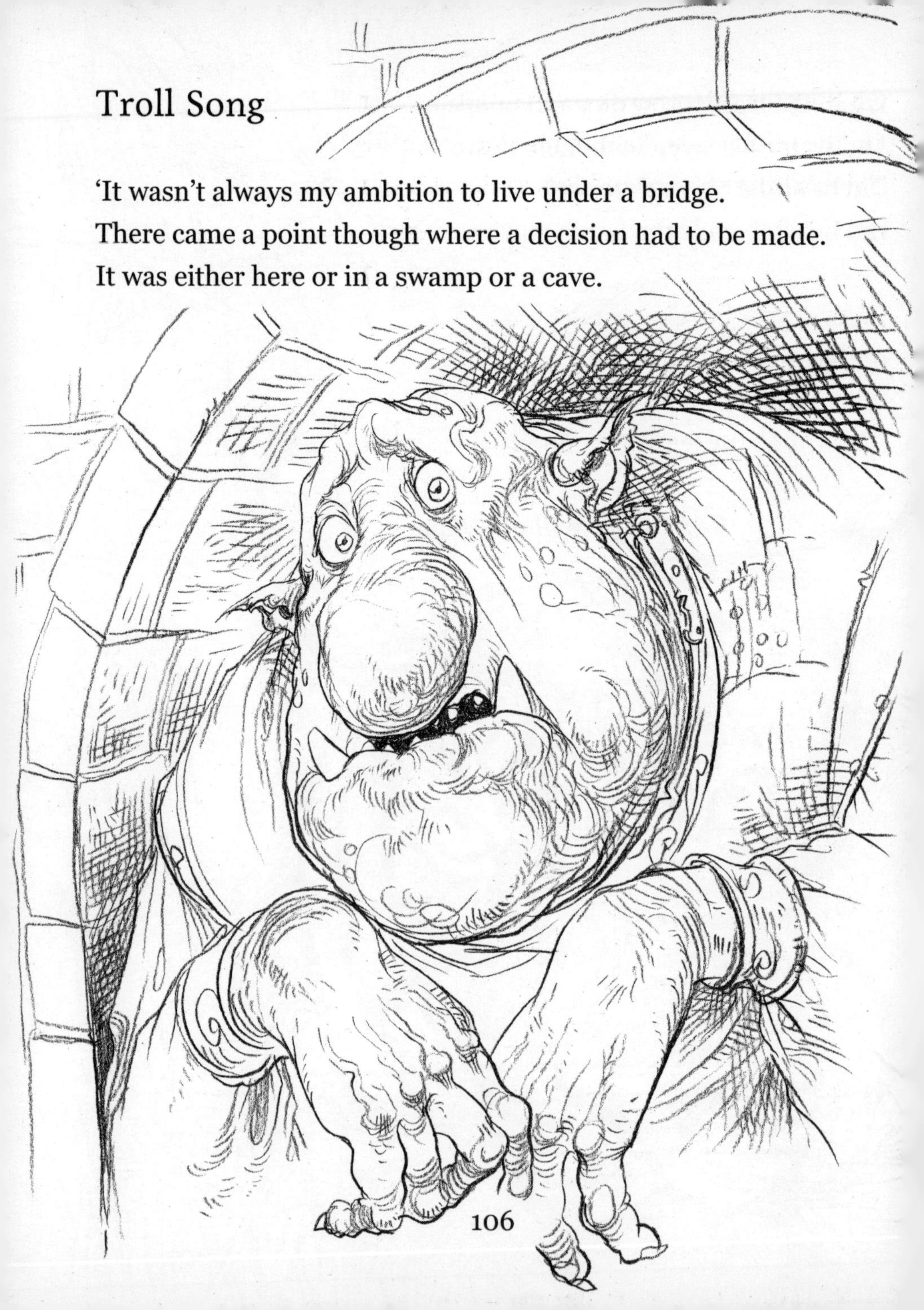

On the plus side, there's cold running water all the time.
On the minus side, I am living under a bridge.
There's little privacy and less in the way of respect.

It's only a small bridge. My feet stick out when I sleep.
I bang my head more than I'd like.
I get into arguments with ducks.

People look down on me, living under a bridge.
But it's a tradition, my mum said, and tradition's tradition.
Sometimes I eat the ducks. Those are arguments I've won.

On either river bank are pastures. Lush-lands.
I like the smell in spring of the hundred different flowers.
I never mention this when other trolls come to visit.

I read a lot of books. They contain other worlds.
For a time I can imagine I'm not living under a bridge.
You can learn things in books too, important useful things:
I eat every goat I see these days, just to be on the safe side.'

A. F. Harrold

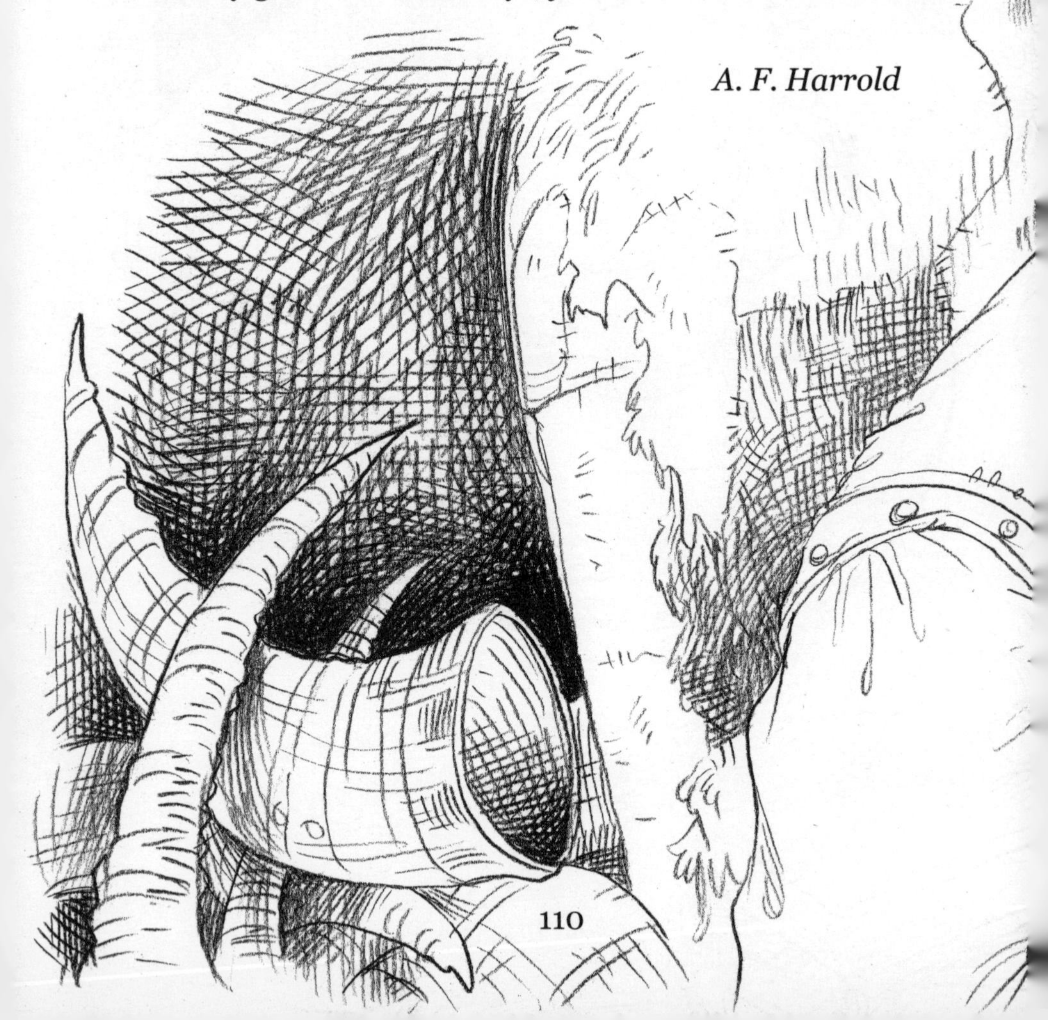

The Walrus and the Carpenter

The sun was shining on the sea,
 Shining with all his might:
He did his very best to make
 The billows smooth and bright –
And this was odd, because it was
 The middle of the night.

The moon was shining sulkily,
 Because she thought the sun
Had got no business to be there
 After the day was done –
'It's very rude of him,' she said,
 'To come and spoil the fun!'

The sea was wet as wet could be,
 The sands were dry as dry.
You could not see a cloud, because
 No cloud was in the sky:
No birds were flying overhead –
 There were no birds to fly.

The Walrus and the Carpenter
    Were walking close at hand;
They wept like anything to see
    Such quantities of sand:
'If this were only cleared away,'
    They said, 'it would be grand!'

'If seven maids with seven mops
    Swept it for half a year,
Do you suppose,' the Walrus said,
    'That they could get it clear?'
'I doubt it,' said the Carpenter,
    And shed a bitter tear.

'O Oysters, come and walk with us!'
The Walrus did beseech.
'A pleasant walk, a pleasant talk,
Along the briny beach:
We cannot do with more than four,
To give a hand to each.'

The eldest Oyster looked at him,
But never a word he said:
The eldest Oyster winked his eye,
And shook his heavy head —
Meaning to say he did not choose
To leave the oyster-bed.

But four young Oysters hurried up,
    All eager for the treat:
Their coats were brushed, their faces washed,
    Their shoes were clean and neat –
And this was odd, because, you know,
    They hadn't any feet.

Four other Oysters followed them,
    And yet another four;
And thick and fast they came at last,
    And more, and more, and more –
All hopping through the frothy waves,
    And scrambling to the shore.

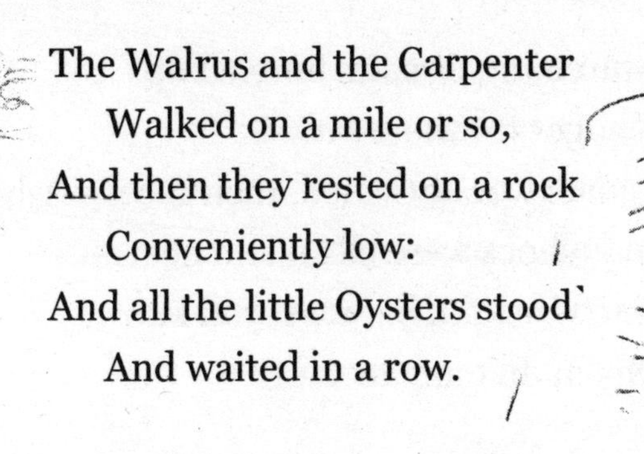

The Walrus and the Carpenter
Walked on a mile or so,
And then they rested on a rock
Conveniently low:
And all the little Oysters stood
And waited in a row.

'The time has come,' the Walrus said,
'To talk of many things:
Of shoes — and ships — and sealing-wax —
Of cabbages — and kings —
And why the sea is boiling hot —
And whether pigs have wings.'

'But wait a bit,' the Oysters cried,
    'Before we have our chat;
For some of us are out of breath,
    And all of us are fat!'
'No hurry!' said the Carpenter.
    They thanked him much for that.

'A loaf of bread,' the Walrus said,
    'Is what we chiefly need:
Pepper and vinegar besides
    Are very good indeed —
Now, if you're ready, Oysters dear,
    We can begin to feed.'

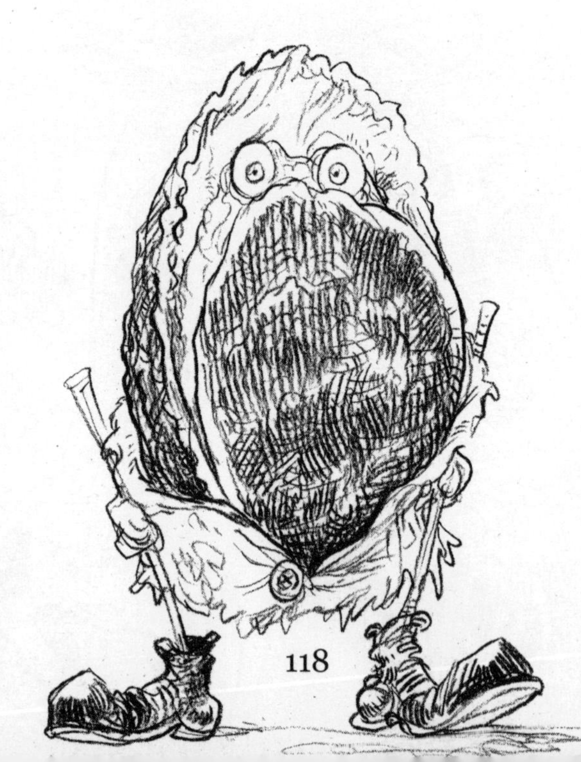

'But not on us!' the Oysters cried,
Turning a little blue.
'After such kindness, that would be
A dismal thing to do!'
'The night is fine,' the Walrus said.
'Do you admire the view?

'It was so kind of you to come!
And you are very nice!'
The Carpenter said nothing but
'Cut us another slice.
I wish you were not quite so deaf —
I've had to ask you twice!'

'It seems a shame,' the Walrus said,
'To play them such a trick,
After we've brought them out so far,
And made them trot so quick!'
The Carpenter said nothing but
'The butter's spread too thick!'

'I weep for you,' the Walrus said:
'I deeply sympathize.'
With sobs and tears he sorted out
Those of the largest size,
Holding his pocket-handkerchief
Before his streaming eyes.

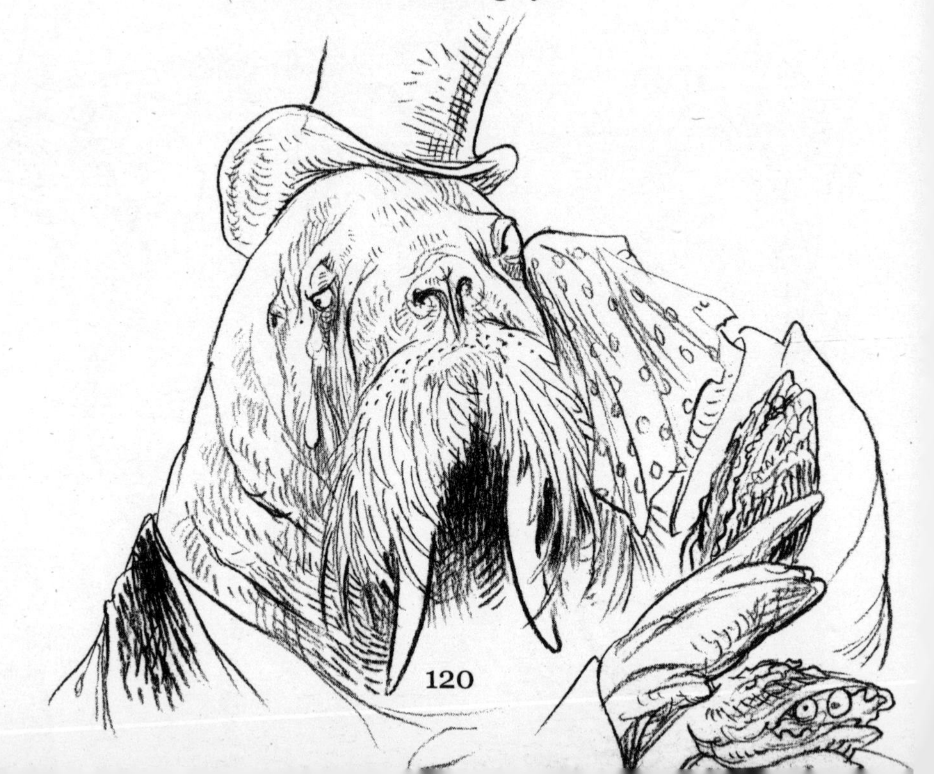

'O Oysters,' said the Carpenter,
'You've had a pleasant run!
Shall we be trotting home again?'
But answer came there none –
And this was scarcely odd, because
They'd eaten every one.

Lewis Carroll

Turvy-Topsy

Gentlemen and Ladies, all and one,
Let's have a little games and fun.

I've noticed that the things we say,
Sound wrong if said a different way.

I've never wandered forth and back,
Never been beaten blue and black.

And through my life, large and by,
I've yet to be left dry and high.

Error and trial, punishment and crime,
It's go and touch, again and time.

My fortunes are not down and up.
I never drink from a saucer and cup.

No pepper and salt upon my dish
Of bacon and liver or chips and fish . . .

Under key and lock . . . Order and law . . .
All bothered and hot . . . Peace and war . . .

Simple and pure, though it may sound dull,
It's how it sounds makes it void and null.

You shouldn't mix pleasure with business:
The bees and the birds with the M & S.

Mind your qs and ps come shine or rain,
And try not to get it wrong again.

Cos, wrong or right, to return to food;
"Where's the fork 'n knife?" just sounds kind of rude.

Paul Stewart

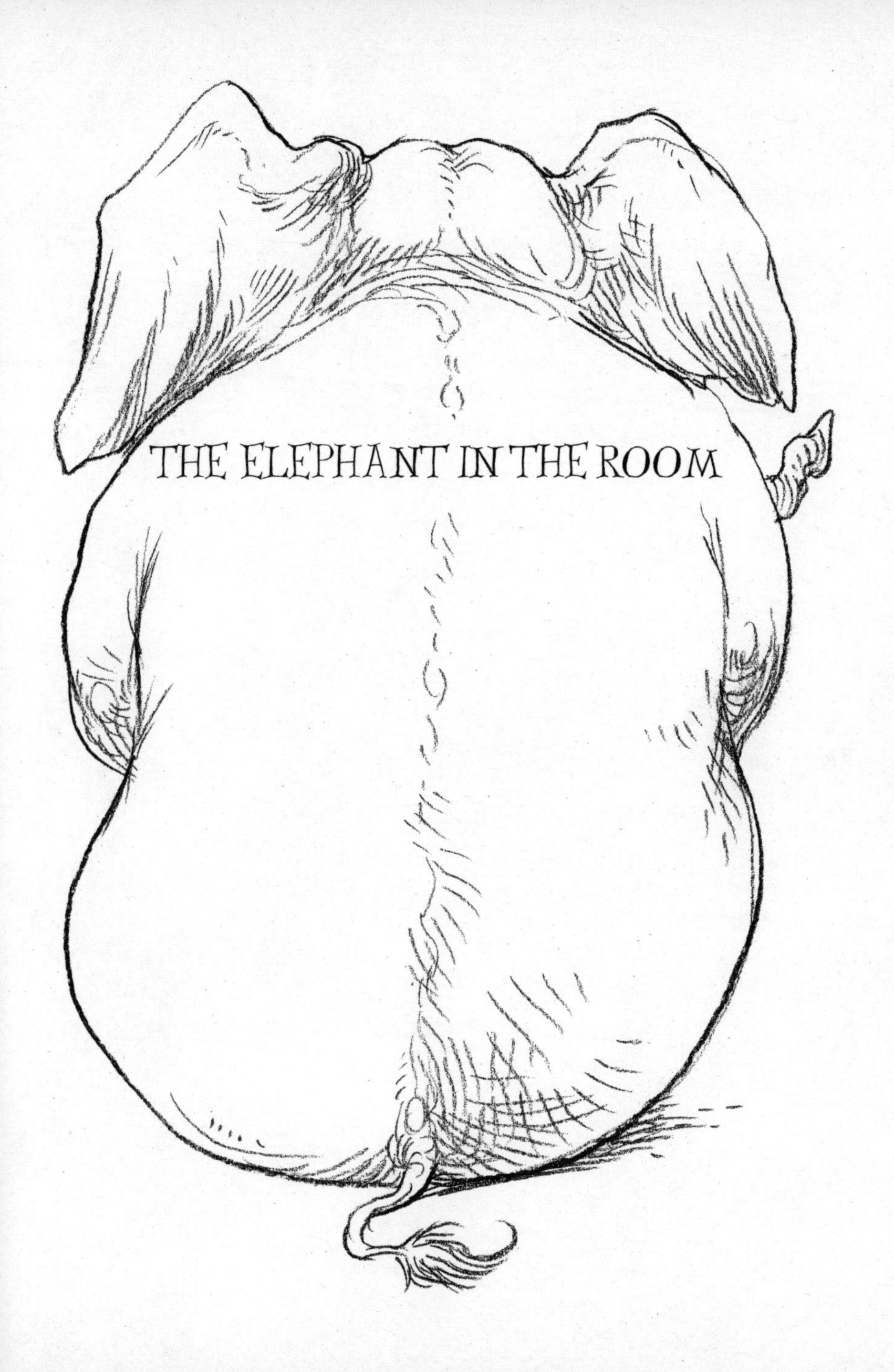

THE ELEPHANT IN THE ROOM

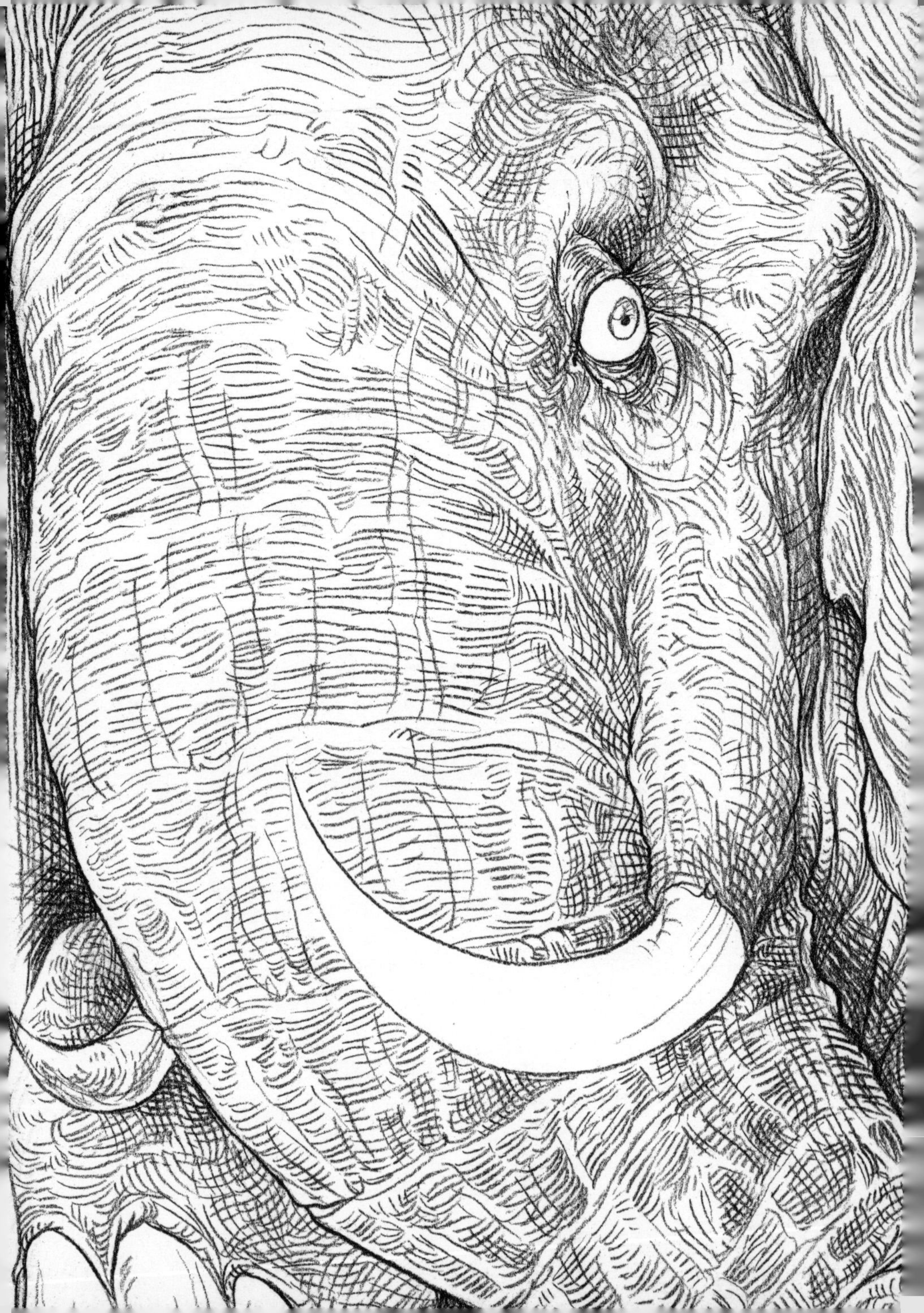

The Elephant in the Room

The room is
almost all
elephant.
Almost none
of it isn't.
Pretty much
solid elephant.
So there's no
room to talk
about it.

Kay Ryan

Bad New Government

Love, I woke in an empty flat to a bad new government;
it was cold the fridge was still empty my heart, that junkie,
was still chomping on the old fuel *vroom*, I start the day
like a tired
  motorcyclist I want to go very fast and email you about
the following
happy circumstances: early rosebuds, a birthday party, a new
cake recipe but
  today it's hot water bottles and austerity breakfast and my
toast burns in protest

You are not here of course but you live in me like a tiny valve of a man
you light up my chambers   Later I will call to tell you about the new
  prime minister,   the worrying new developments   and about how
I am writing my first political poem   which is also (always) about my love for you

Emily Berry

No Man Is an Island

No man is an island entire of itself; every man
is a piece of the continent, a part of the main;
if a clod be washed away by the sea, Europe
is the less, as well as if a promontory were, as
well as any manor of thy friends or of thine
own were; any man's death diminishes me,
because I am involved in mankind.
And therefore never send to know for whom
the bell tolls; it tolls for thee.

John Donne

The Gettysburg Address

Four score and seven years ago our fathers brought forth on this continent, a new nation, conceived in Liberty, and dedicated to the proposition that all men are created equal.

Now we are engaged in a great civil war, testing whether that nation, or any nation so conceived and so dedicated, can long endure. We are met on a great battlefield of that war. We have come to dedicate a portion of that field, as a final resting place for those who here gave their lives that that nation might live. It is altogether fitting and proper that we should do this.

But, in a larger sense, we can not dedicate – we can not consecrate – we can not hallow – this ground. The brave men, living and dead, who struggled here, have consecrated it, far above our poor power to add or detract. The world will little note, nor long remember what we say here, but it can never forget what they did here. It is for us the living, rather, to be dedicated here to the unfinished work which they who fought here have thus far so nobly advanced. It is rather for us to be here, dedicated to the great task remaining before us – that from these honored dead we take increased devotion to that cause for which they gave the last full measure of devotion – that we here highly resolve that these dead shall not have died in vain – that this nation, under God, shall have a new birth of freedom – and that government of the people, by the people, for the people, shall not perish from the earth.

Abraham Lincoln

The New Colossus

Not like the brazen giant of Greek fame,
With conquering limbs astride from land to land;
Here at our sea-washed, sunset gates shall stand
A mighty woman with a torch, whose flame
Is the imprisoned lightning, and her name
Mother of Exiles. From her beacon-hand
Glows world-wide welcome; her mild eyes command
The air-bridged harbor that twin cities frame.
'Keep, ancient lands, your storied pomp!' cries she
With silent lips. 'Give me your tired, your poor,
Your huddled masses yearning to breathe free,
The wretched refuse of your teeming shore.
Send these, the homeless, tempest-tost to me,
I lift my lamp beside the golden door!'

Emma Lazarus

In Case of Fire

In case of FIRE break glass

In case of GLASS fill with water

In case of WATER wear heavy boots

In case of HEAVY BOOTS assume foetal position

In case of FOETAL POSITION loosen clothing

In case of CLOTHING avoid nudist beach

In case of NUDIST BEACH keep sand out of eyes

In case of EYES close curtains

In case of CURTAINS switch on light

In case of LIGHT embrace truth

In case of TRUTH spread word

In case of WORD keep mum

In case of MUM open arms

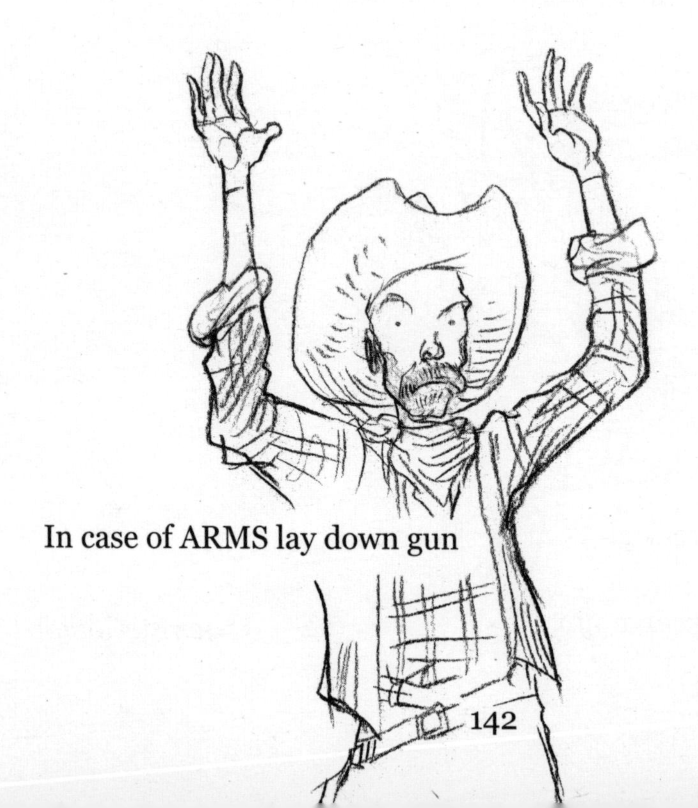

In case of ARMS lay down gun

In case of GUN, fire

In case of FIRE break glass.

Roger McGough

FOR SALE
FOR SALE
FOR SALE
FOR SALE
FOR SALE
FOR SALE
FOR SALE
FOR SALE
STOP THE WAR

We Lived Happily During the War

And when they bombed other people's houses, we

protested
but not enough, we opposed them but not

enough. I was
in my bed, around my bed America

was falling: invisible house by invisible house by invisible house.

I took a chair outside and watched the sun.

In the sixth month
of a disastrous reign in the house of money

in the street of money in the city of money in the country of
money,
our great country of money, we (forgive us)

lived happily during the war.

Ilya Kaminsky

The Second Coming

Turning and turning in the widening gyre
The falcon cannot hear the falconer;
Things fall apart; the centre cannot hold;
Mere anarchy is loosed upon the world,
The blood-dimmed tide is loosed, and everywhere
The ceremony of innocence is drowned;
The best lack all conviction, while the worst
Are full of passionate intensity.

Surely some revelation is at hand;
Surely the Second Coming is at hand.
The Second Coming! Hardly are those words out
When a vast image out of *Spiritus Mundi*
Troubles my sight: somewhere in sands of the desert
A shape with lion body and the head of a man,
A gaze blank and pitiless as the sun,
Is moving its slow thighs, while all about it
Reel shadows of the indignant desert birds.

The darkness drops again; but now I know
That twenty centuries of stony sleep
Were vexed to nightmare by a rocking cradle,
And what rough beast, its hour come round at last,
Slouches towards Bethlehem to be born?

W. B. Yeats

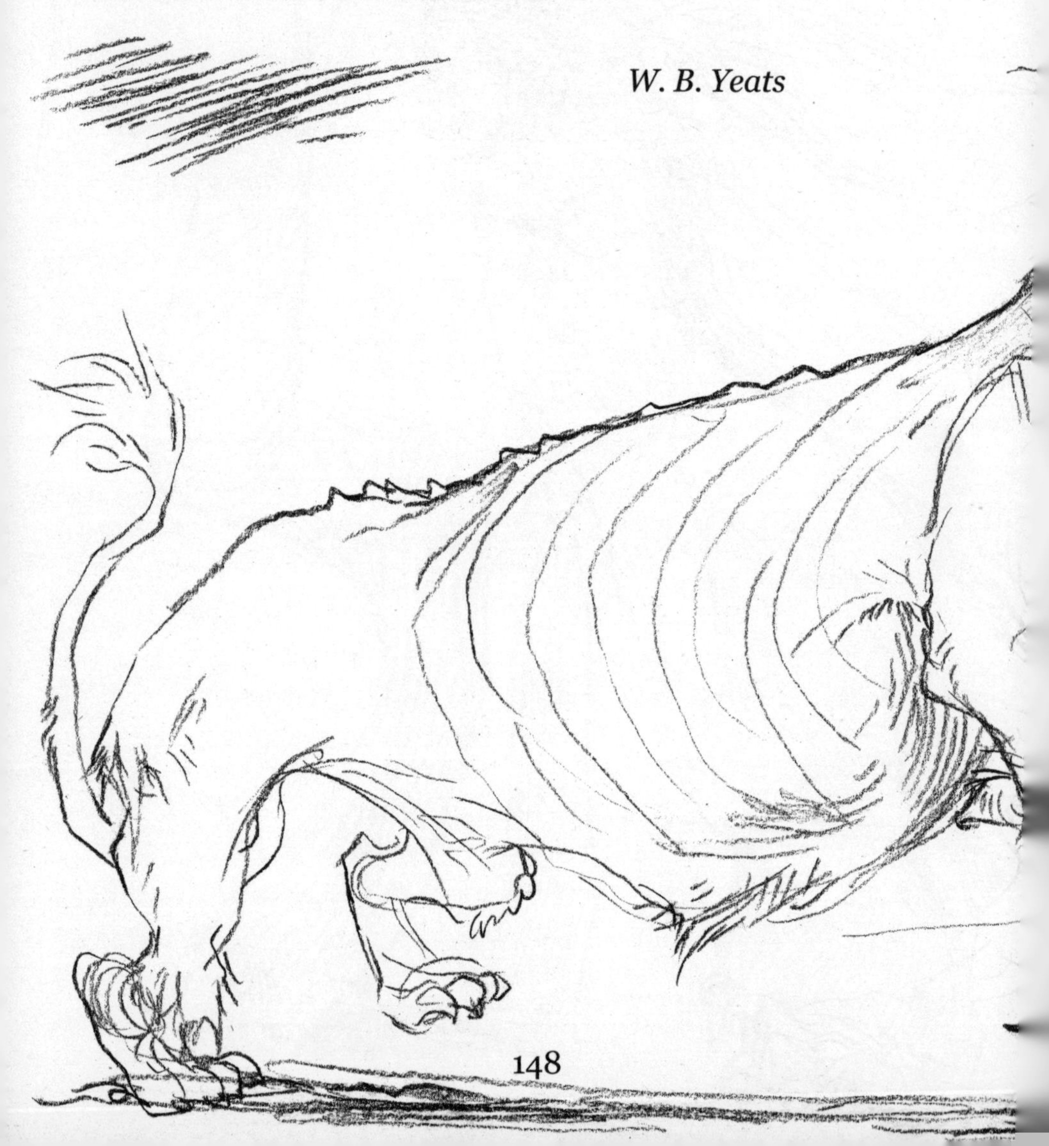

To Pythagoras in the Rain Forest

All things change, but nothing is lost
consoles the wisdom of Pythagoras.
The soul is monkey, orchid, cockatoo,
it passes with the lightest brush,
stirring whatever limb and leaf it must.

But it is harder now to believe
that nothing goes out of this world,
as the loggers bring the canopy down,
and whole layers of livings collapse.
Pythagoras – can the chameleon turn black?

And will our god rain gold upon us?
Will he heat the air to melt the ice-caps?
And will the rain that would have tapped
its secret rhythm on the great green drum
enrich us beyond our wildest dreams?

Recently we wake from the rainforest
crying like lemurs in the lurid dawn.
The axes are cutting deep in the sap,
coming closer to our inviolate patch.
Open your forms, Pythagoras –

we are ready to jump.

Stephen Plaice

Ozymandias

I met a traveller from an antique land
Who said: Two vast and trunkless legs of stone
Stand in the desert . . . Near them, on the sand,
Half sunk a shattered visage lies, whose frown,
And wrinkled lip, and sneer of cold command,
Tell that its sculptor well those passions read
Which yet survive, stamped on these lifeless things,
The hand that mocked them, and the heart that fed:
And on the pedestal, these words appear:
'My name is Ozymandias, king of kings:
Look on my works, ye Mighty, and despair!'
Nothing beside remains. Round the decay
Of that colossal wreck, boundless and bare
The lone and level sands stretch far away.

Percy Bysshe Shelley

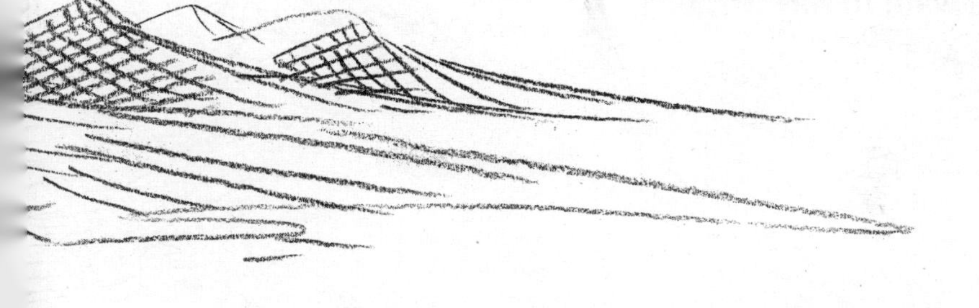

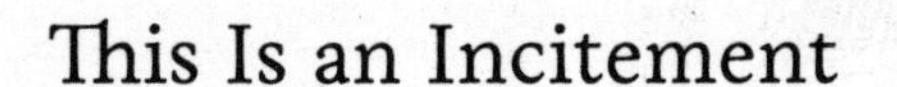

This Is an Incitement

Don't settle into inertia
As the ash falls on your head and shoulders,
Soft and ankle deep at your feet.

Take up your pens and brushes
And make Art.

The ancient dragons of greed
Coiled tight around their hoards
Don't understand Art.
But the snake oil minions
Who whisper in their ears as they sleep,
They fear it.

Art can capture the souls
They bought and paid for.
If you want to slay dragons,
Make Art.

Chris Riddell

Remains: A Song

Love will not survive us,
or not survive us long –
in time it dwindles out
and all those we loved are gone.

Washed clean with fresh forgetting
the world will hurtle on –
for love will not survive us,
or not survive us long.

We know the dead a little,
as we take them at their word –
trace our likenesses by mouth,
repeating what we've heard.

Though souls are lost to history,
turned to dust, not into birds,
we can know the dead a little –
in the end there is the word.

Only marks we make remain:
take Chauvet, take Lascaux –
graffiti, say, and petroglyphs
stay behind us when we go.

And so we write our letters,
write our books because we know
that only marks we make remain:
see Chauvet, see Lascaux.

A. F. Harrold

LOCKDOWN

Serenity Prayer

Send me a slow news day,
A quiet, subdued day,
in which nothing much happens of note,
save for the passing of time,
the consumption of wine,
and a re-run of *Murder, She Wrote*.

Grant me a no news day,
A spare-me-your-views day,
in which nothing much happens at all,
except a few hours together,
some regional weather,
a day we can barely recall.

Brian Bilston

Home-Thoughts from Abroad

Oh, to be in England
Now that April's there,
And whoever wakes in England
Sees, some morning, unaware,
That the lowest boughs and the brushwood sheaf
Round the elm-tree bole are in tiny leaf,
While the chaffinch sings on the orchard bough
In England – now!

And after April, when May follows,
And the whitethroat builds, and all the swallows!
Hark, where my blossomed pear-tree in the hedge
Leans to the field and scatters on the clover
Blossoms and dewdrops – at the bent spray's edge –
That's the wise thrush; he sings each song twice over,
Lest you should think he never could recapture
The first fine careless rapture!
And though the fields look rough with hoary dew,
All will be gay when noontide wakes anew
The buttercups, the little children's dower
– Far brighter than this gaudy melon-flower!

Robert Browning

Lockdown

I sat beneath the May moon last night
and missed my life,
in silver and shadow with
a distant trundling of trains
going nowhere.

There was a muted tranquillity in
sitting in the midnight garden,
my lockdown house silent
and sleeping behind me.

Then you came down the stairs
and noticing the open door
stepped out to join me in the
moonlight.
'Oh, it's you, Dad,' you said, smiling.

And suddenly I was falling away into empty darkness,
mourning the life you were missing so bravely.

Chris Riddell

Love in the Time of Coronavirus

Today, we stockpile empathy.
We supply love and good energy.
We sing to each other across buildings.
We say 'I love you' through social distancing.

Do you know that writing letters
to our friends is back in fashion?
And that we finally have time to read more books,
whether historical or fiction?

My cousin told me she hadn't seen
such a blue sky in her city before.
My uncle went on his first walk in the woods.
He heard a bird sing for the first time since he went to war.

Even in sickness, this world
is allowed to be beautiful.
And we are still allowed to love it,
for there is always room for hope.

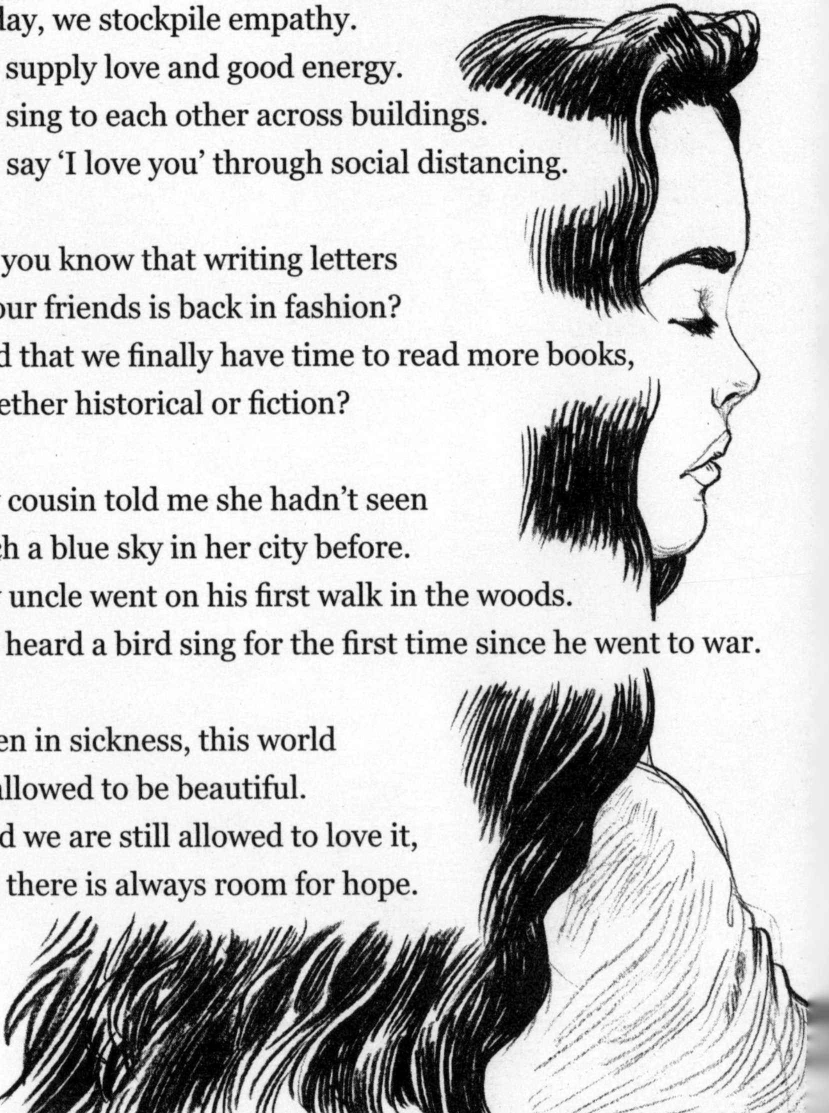

This is just me checking in
sending you the moon as a poem,
praying and wishing for us all
a speedy recovery.

And if nothing else,
There will always be poetry.
We will always have poetry.

Nikita Gill

Miracles

Why, who makes much of a miracle?
As to me I know of nothing else but miracles,
Whether I walk the streets of Manhattan,
Or dart my sight over the roofs of houses toward the sky,
Or wade with naked feet along the beach just in the edge
of the water,

Or stand under trees in the woods,
Or talk by day with any one I love, or sleep in the bed at night
with any one I love,

Or sit at table at dinner with the rest,
Or look at strangers opposite me riding in the car,
Or watch honey-bees busy around the hive of a
  summer forenoon,
Or animals feeding in the fields,
Or birds, or the wonderfulness of insects in the air,
Or the wonderfulness of the sundown, or of stars
  shining so quiet and bright,
Or the exquisite delicate thin curve of the new
  moon in spring;
These with the rest, one and all, are to me miracles,
The whole referring, yet each distinct and in its place.

To me every hour of the light and dark is a miracle,
Every cubic inch of space is a miracle,
Every square yard of the surface of the earth is
spread with the same,
Every foot of the interior swarms with the same.
To me the sea is a continual miracle,
The fishes that swim – the rocks – the motion of
the waves – the ships with men in them,
What stranger miracles are there?

Walt Whitman

The Perfect Place

The world is the perfect place to be born into.
Unless of course, you don't like people
or trees, or stars, or baguettes.

Its secret is movement.
As soon as you have stepped back
to admire the scenery
or opened your mouth
to sing its praises
it has changed places with itself.

Infinitesimally, perhaps,
but those infinitesimals add up.

(About the baguettes,
that was just me being silly.)

Roger McGough

An Instinct of Hope

Is there another world for this frail dust
To warm with life and be itself again?
Something about me daily speaks there must,
And why should instinct nourish hopes in vain?

’Tis nature’s prophecy that such will be,
And everything seems struggling to explain
The close sealed volume of its mystery.

Time wandering onward keeps its usual pace
As seeming anxious of eternity,
To meet that calm and find a resting place.
E'en the small violet feels a future power
And waits each year renewing blooms to bring,
And surely man is no inferior flower
To die unworthy of a second spring?

John Clare

FOR
SALE

Good Bones

Life is short, though I keep this from my children.
Life is short, and I've shortened mine
in a thousand delicious, ill-advised ways,
a thousand deliciously ill-advised ways
I'll keep from my children. The world is at least
fifty percent terrible, and that's a conservative
estimate, though I keep this from my children.
For every bird there is a stone thrown at a bird.
For every loved child, a child broken, bagged,
sunk in a lake. Life is short and the world
is at least half terrible, and for every kind
stranger, there is one who would break you,
though I keep this from my children. I am trying
to sell them the world. Any decent realtor,
walking you through a real shithole, chirps on
about good bones: This place could be beautiful,
right? You could make this place beautiful.

Maggie Smith

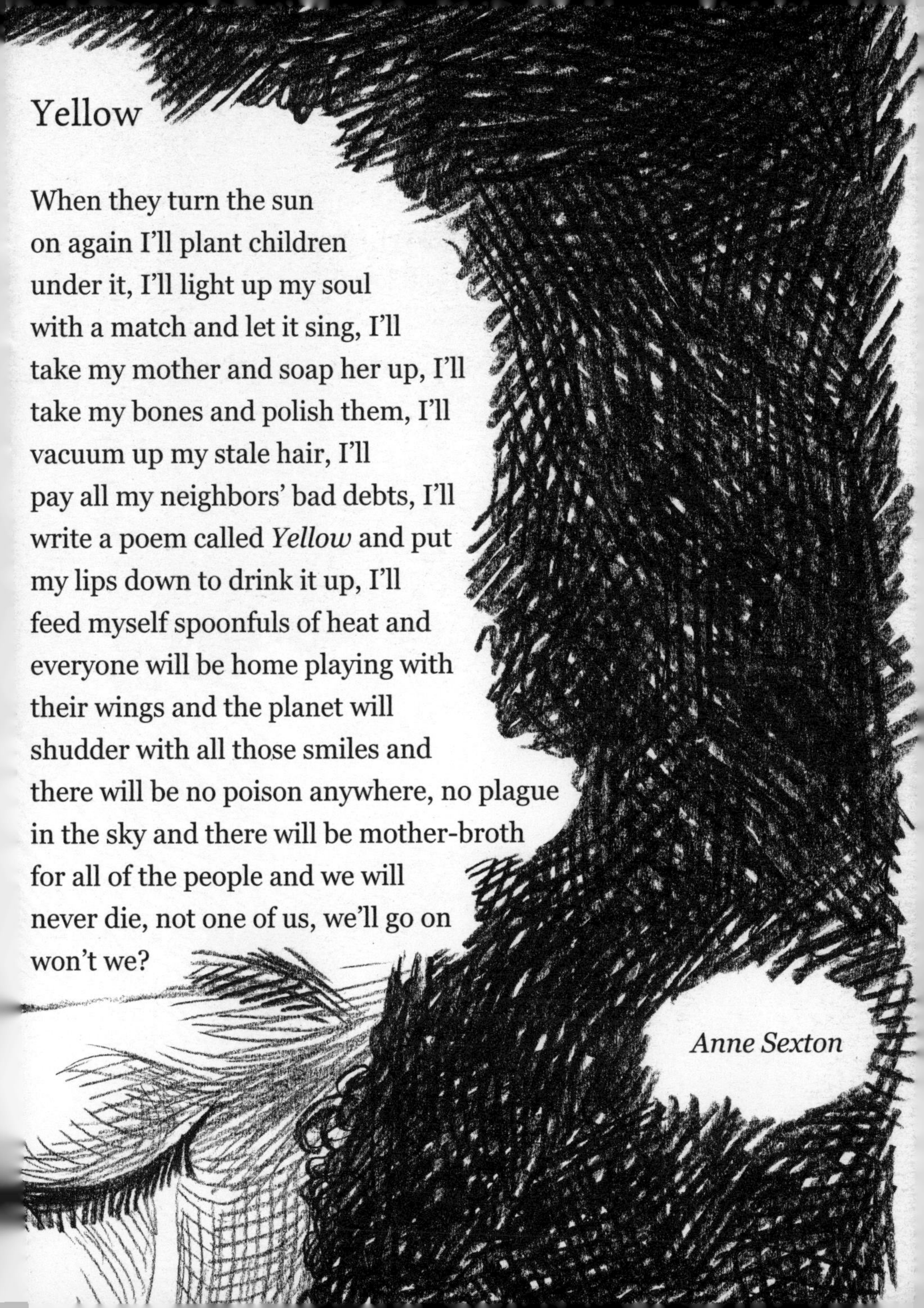

Yellow

When they turn the sun
on again I'll plant children
under it, I'll light up my soul
with a match and let it sing, I'll
take my mother and soap her up, I'll
take my bones and polish them, I'll
vacuum up my stale hair, I'll
pay all my neighbors' bad debts, I'll
write a poem called *Yellow* and put
my lips down to drink it up, I'll
feed myself spoonfuls of heat and
everyone will be home playing with
their wings and the planet will
shudder with all those smiles and
there will be no poison anywhere, no plague
in the sky and there will be mother-broth
for all of the people and we will
never die, not one of us, we'll go on
won't we?

Anne Sexton

from Endymion

A thing of beauty is a joy for ever:
Its loveliness increases; it will never
Pass into nothingness; but still will keep
A bower quiet for us, and a sleep
Full of sweet dreams, and health, and quiet breathing.

Therefore, on every morrow, are we wreathing
A flowery band to bind us to the earth,
Spite of despondence, of the inhuman dearth
Of noble natures, of the gloomy days,
Of all the unhealthy and
  o'er-darkened ways
Made for our searching: yes, in spite of all,

Some shape of beauty moves away the pall
From our dark spirits. Such the sun, the moon,
Trees old, and young, sprouting a shady boon
For simple sheep; and such are daffodils
With the green world they live in; and clear rills
That for themselves a cooling covert make
'Gainst the hot season; the mid forest brake,
Rich with a sprinkling of fair musk-rose blooms:

And such too is the grandeur of the dooms
We have imagined for the mighty dead;
All lovely tales that we have heard or read:
An endless fountain of immortal drink,
Pouring unto us from the heaven's brink.

John Keats

Lochan

(for Jean Johnstone)

When all this is over I mean
to travel north, by the high

drove roads and cart tracks
probably in June,

with the gentle dog-roses
flourishing beside me. I mean

to find among the thousands
scattered in that land

a certain lochan,
Where water lilies rise

like small fat moons,
and tied among the reeds,

underneath a rowan,
a white boat waits.

Kathleen Jamie

Index of First Lines

Index of Poets

Acknowledgements

The compiler and publisher would like to thank the following for permission to use their copyright material:

Antrobus, Raymond: 'Happy Birthday Moon' from *The Perseverance* (Penned in the Margins, 2018). Copyright © Raymond Antrobus, 2018. Used with permission of the publisher; **Benson, Fiona:** 'Almond Blosson' from *Vertigo and Ghost* (Jonathon Cape, 2019). Copyright © Fiona Benson, 2019. Used with permission of the publisher; **Berry, Emily:** 'Bad New Government' from *Dear Boy* (Faber & Faber, 2013). Copyright © Emily Berry, 2013. Used with permission of the publisher; **Berry, Wendell:** 'The Peace of Wild Things' from *The Peace of Wild Things* (Penguin, 2018). Copyright © Wendell Berry, 2018. Used with permission of the publisher; **Bilston, Brian:** 'Serenity Prayer' by Brian Bilston. Copyright © Brian Bilston. Used with kind permission of the poet; **Daryani, Khushi:** 'My Lover Eats Words for Supper' by Khushi Daryani. First published by The Poetry Society for the Foyle Young Poets of the Year Award 2019, www.foyleyoungpoets.org. Copyright © Khushi Daryani, 2019. Used with kind permission of the poet and The Poetry Society, **Elson, Rebecca:** 'The Hubble Space Telescope Before Repair' from *A Responsibility to Awe* (Carcanet, 2018). Copyright © Rebecca Elson, 2018. Used with permission of the publisher; **Gaiman, Neil:** 'What You Need to be Warm' by Neil Gaiman was originally written in support of UNHCR's Winter Emergency Appeal. Copyright © 2019 by UNHCR, the UN Refugee Agency. Reprinted by permission of Writers House LLC acting as agent for the author and UNHCR; 'The Mushroom Hunters'. Copyright © Neil Gaiman, 2017. Reprinted by permission of Writers House LLC acting as agent for the author; **Gill, Nikita:** 'Kindness' and 'Love in the Time of Coronavirus' by Nikita Gill. Copyright © Nikita Gill, 2020. Used with permission of the agent on behalf of the poet; **Harrold, A.F.:** 'Troll Song' from *Things You Find in a Poet's Beard* (Burning Eye Books, 2015) and 'Remains' first published here. Copyright © A.F. Harrold, 2020. Reproduced by kind permission of the poet; **Jamie, Kathleen:** 'Lochen' from *Jizzen* (Picador, 1999). Copyright © Kathleen Jamie, 1999. Used with permission of the publisher; **Kaminsky, Ilya:** 'We Lived Happily During the War' from *Deaf Republic* (Faber & Faber, 2019). Copyright © Ilya Kaminsky, 2019. Used with permission of the publisher; **Kennard, Luke:** 'Crow Baby' first published in *The Scores Journal*, Dec 2019. Copyright © Luke Kennard, 2019. Used with kind permission of the author; **Kenyon, Jane:** 'Otherworld' by Jane Kenyon. Copyright © the Estate of Jane Kenyon, 1995. Used with permission of the publisher, Graywolf Press; **Limón, Ada:** 'The Raincoat' from *The Carrying* (Corsair, 2019). Copyright © Ada Limón, 2019. Used with permission of the publisher; **Lines, Nadia:** 'Explaining Memes to Keats' by Nadia Lines. First published by The Poetry Society for the Foyle Young Poets of the Year Award 2019, www.foyleyoungpoets.org. Copyright © Nadia Lines, 2019. Used with kind permission of the poet and The Poetry Society; **McGough, Roger:** 'In Case of Fire' and 'The Perfect Place'. Copyright © Roger McGough. Used with permission of the agent; **Oliver, Mary:** 'Wild Geese' (Grove Atlantic). Copyright © The Estate of Mary Oliver. Used with permission of the Publisher; **Plaice, Stephen:** 'To Pythagoras in the Rain Forest' from *Over the Rollers* (Yorick Books, 1992). Copyright © Stephan Plaice, 1992. Used with kind permission of the author; **Rooney, Rachel:** 'Battle Call' and 'No Man's Land'. Copyright © Rachel Rooney. Used with kind permission of the author; **Russell, Libby:** 'A Word of Advice' by Libby Russell. First published by The Poetry Society for the Foyle Young Poets of the Year Award 2019, www.foyleyoungpoets.org. Copyright © Libby Russell. Used with kind permission of the poet and The Poetry Society; **Ryan, Kay:** 'The Elephant in the Room' from *Erratic Facts* (Grove Press/Atlantic Monthly Press, 2015). Copyright © Kay Ryan, 2015. Used with permission of the publisher; **Sexton, Anne:** 'Yellow' from *Mercies: Selected Poems* (Penguin Classics, 2020). Copyright © Anne Sexton. Used with permission of the publisher; **Smith, Maggie:** 'Good Bones' from *Good Bones: Poems* (Tupelo Press, 2017). Copyright © Maggie Smith, 2017. Reprinted with the permission of The Permissions Company, LLC, on behalf of Tupelo Press, tupelopress.org; **Sorescu, Marin:** 'With Only One Life' by Marin Sorescu, trns. Joana Russell-Gebbelt and D. J. Enright from *The Biggest Egg in the World* (Bloodaxe Books, 1997). Translation copyright © Joana Russell-Gebbelt and D. J. Enright, 1997. Used with kind permission of the publisher; **Stewart, Paul:** 'Turvy Topsy' by Paul Stewart. Copyright © Paul Stewart. Used with kind permission of the author;

Every effort has been made to trace the copyright holders, but if any have been inadvertently overlooked the publisher will be pleased to make the necessary arrangement at the first opportunity.

About the Book

This gorgeous collection will ignite your inner activist and provide comfort in uncertain times. These poems speak of hope, happiness, rebellion and living through a pandemic and are brought to life with Chris's exquisite, intricate artwork.

It features famous poems, old and new, and a few surprises. Includes poems from Neil Gaiman, Nikita Gill, Maggie Smith, Brian Bilston, Raymond Antrobus, Lewis Carroll and many more.

About Chris Riddell

Chris Riddell, the 2015–2017 UK Children's Laureate, is an accomplished artist and the political cartoonist for the *Observer*. He has enjoyed great acclaim for his books for children. His books have won a number of major prizes, including the 2001, 2004 and 2016 CILIP Kate Greenaway Medals. *Goth Girl and the Ghost of a Mouse* won the Costa Children's Book Award in 2013. His previous work for Macmillan includes the bestselling Ottoline books, *The Emperor of Absurdia*, and, with Paul Stewart, Muddle Earth and the Scavenger series. Chris lives in Brighton with his family.